By

Mary Hill

EASTON, PA

The Gift   Mary Hill

FIRST ORR BOOKS EDITION, 2008

Copyright © 2008 Mary Hill

All rights reserved. No part of this book may be
reproduced, scanned, distributed in any printed or
electronic form, except for the inclusion of brief quotations
in review, without permission in writing from the
author/publisher.

The Gift/ Mary Hill

ISBN 978-0-9800611-7-8

Author photo © 2008

Original oil painting in cover art by Mary Hill

Printed in the United States of America

10 9 8 7 6 5 4 3 2 1

Praise for Mary Hill's Book

Mary Hill's THE GIFT is a breezy, single-sitting read dedicated to helping others live triumphantly despite physical adversities. It is a work of encouragement and hope for those, like the author, living with incurable diseases.

Hill's book is a nice balance of spiritual and practical insights, making it a likely conversation piece. For this reason THE GIFT is well suited for Bible study, coffee table, or support groups. At the same time, the author's folksy style gives THE GIFT the texture of a personalized self-help guide. Throughout, the reader gets the sense that Mary Hill has pulled him or her aside to share her experiences, friend to friend.

Appropriately titled, THE GIFT is recommended reading, if for no other reason, than because of its "we'll-get-through-this-thing-together" feel.

Review by Carolina Summers Book Reviews
www.carolinasummers.com

DEDICATION

I want to dedicate this book to my wonderful husband, three children, their spouses, and seven grand children. They are the light of my life.
I want to thank all my dear friends who have been there for me in my time of need. I love you all. Thanks for your support and love.

FORWARD

Mary Hill has the one unique, personal quality that everyone admires—She loves life. And her love for life is contagious.

Mary views every aspect of life as an adventure – the good, the bad, the joy and the pain. God has used this quality in Mary to make the difference in her life, and in the lives of those she encounters.

Every conversation I have with Mary confirms to me that she is real. She doesn't hide the hurts and she doesn't minimize the joy. She is truly alive.

As you read her life story, you will realize – in spite of her pain and "incurable" disease – that she has been given a gift.

And, if you listen closely, you'll discover that you have been given the gift of life as well!

Al Giles
Associate Pastor
Trinity Evangelical Congregational Church
Boyertown PA

NOTE FROM THE AUTHOR

This book was written with love for those who have or know someone diagnosed with an incurable disease. I wish I could sit down with you for a cup of tea and meet you in person. We could look out my kitchen window and see the mountains painted with the colors of the setting sun. Since we can't, this is the next best option.

The reason for this book can be summed up in two words: *encouragement* and *hope*. That's my *goal*. I was diagnosed with Parkinson's eight years ago. I had a massive heart attack three years ago, a triple bypass operation with the insertion of triple stents. Stents are placed strategically in narrowed or weakened arteries in a procedure known as an angioplasty. This operation helps prevent arteries from becoming narrowed or blocked again in the months or years following the operation. Obviously my condition was pretty grave.

Having experienced this procedure and because of my continuing battle with Parkinson's I feel qualified to write about living every day with an incurable disease, and living what I call "the gift of life."

I am not cured. I'm coping with a myriad of physical and mental problems, one day at a time. Each and every day when I rise I'm presented with the opportunity to play a part in finding new solutions, in combating the progression of this disease, in being an advocate for it's survivability, and in keeping it's symptoms at bay as much as possible. Despite the hardship, I have faith that one day I may be cured of Parkinson's and my cardiac issues. More than anything, I'd love it if you'd consider my experiences and be able to draw some strength from them. It would please me to know that I could help you to gain even just a little more faith in your own struggle with Parkinson's, or anything else for that matter.

I don't know what the future holds for you or me, but I think I have some valuable insights to share. Let's start with the premise that you *can* consider your illness a gift.

CHAPTER ONE

Every one of us is given the gift of life. Some people are granted a few seconds. Others are given over a hundred years. It is a precious gift, one that only comes around once. What you **do** with that gift is the important thing.

What are you doing with that precious gift?

Perhaps you're living your life, feeling good and looking good—at least for the most part. Maybe you've never given a second thought to the fact that today could be the last day of your life. I don't say this to scare you as much as I intend to motivate you to "seize the day."

Health is such a fragile gift. It's time that you understand that fact. I came to understand that fact when my life as I knew it came to an end. It could happen to you, you know.

For a moment I want you to consider what it would be like for the world, as you have known it to come to an end. Life as you knew it has changed forever and you've started down an extremely unpredictable road, fraught with twists and turns, pain and sorrow. It is a journey not of your choosing.

I'm on a journey that I certainly would not choose for myself, but one I am destined to live.

Nevertheless, I have a strong faith in God, and He has imbued me with a fighting spirit. I remember my dad, when he was dying and the doctor told him to get his affairs in order, as he didn't have long to live. He jumped up and exclaimed, "You took the Hippocratic oath to help me. If you've given up on me then I'll find a new doctor." This stubborn spirit is what got him through four heart attacks. After each attack the doctors would have the same remark, "I don't know what's keeping him alive."

I have met people of all ages and stages of disease that are fighters and survivors. What they share in common is important to us who have been plagues with a debilitating illness.

They have a strong will to overcome. They struggle every day. They triumph every day because they have not submitted to the enslaving nature of disease. They have a disease, but the disease doesn't have them.

I am convinced that we can learn from their experiences and live life triumphantly. We have to learn how to live out the rest of our days, as happy and meaningful as possible. So lets take this journey together.

CHAPTER TWO

My Story

I was born in Philadelphia in 1951, to Doris and Charles Donnellon. My mother, father and brother all welcomed me into this world. Well maybe not my brother Richard, he was 7 years old at the time of my birth and I'm sure he wanted a brother, not a sister. Nevertheless he took it in stride.

I had a nice childhood though we did not have much in the way of material things. On the other hand we did have love. I was so lucky to have such a wonderful mom and dad. I had wonderful Aunts, uncles and cousins, with whom I spent my summers. I will always cherish those times.

One special childhood memory involves the sweltering, humid summer nights in Philadelphia. I would lie in my bedroom with no air-conditioning and no fans. Sounds would rise up to my open window—the comforting sounds of my dad listening to Phillies games on the radio.

Growing up in the city presented quite a few challenges and difficulties. Still, the Lord was faithful and helped me to get through them all.

My mom took me to church every Sunday. My faith became stronger, and I am forever grateful to her for taking me to this place where I could develop an inner strength and meet my personal Lord and Savior, Jesus Christ.

It was at church that I got to know Danny Hill, my future husband. To this day, I like to tease him, saying that we slept together as babies. Can you believe it? Our mom's put us in the same crib in the nursery. I guess we were destined to be together.

Danny's sister, Eileen was my Pioneer Girl leader (like girl scouts). When I was a teenager we moved to Northeast Philadelphia. I have a good friend that I made at that time. Her name is Merrily. Merrilly is still a close friend. In high school we hung together.

During high school I got to know Danny better. We went to church functions together too. One Christmas Danny invited me to our church's formal dinner. It was not until the Christmas banquet, the following year, that he invited me again. In between we did not see much of each other. We began dating after the second banquet. Later that year we started going steady. We were engaged at 19 and married at 20. Dan obtained a degree in electrical engineering from Penn State and accepted a job at Philadelphia Electric. I got a job at Philadelphia Electric as a customer service representative. We were married June 12, 1971.

Our wedding was beautiful. My dad had saved for this day and wanted to make it special. President Nixon's daughter, Tricia, was married on that same day, in the famous Rose Garden ceremony. Our wedding was just as beautiful and memorable as hers. My parents were so proud, and they loved Dan. I loved Dan's parents and his sister Eileen. Our parents got along. Everything was great. We went to Hawaii for fifteen days for our honeymoon.

Three children later…

Our oldest is Janet, our middle Stephen and youngest David. They are the delights of my heart. I loved raising the children. I didn't work outside the house until my children were older. I had many challenges during those years raising my children. My middle son, Steve had asthma. I spent many nights holding him, as he had trouble breathing. I got to know my local hospital very well, as he and I spent many days and nights there.

When David was a little baby he had surgery, at only three months old. These are just a few examples of difficult times, but most of the days were good.

I took care of my parents until they both passed away. We had good times with them. I spent a lot of time with them, and to this day I thank God for that opportunity.

Outside of the home, I spent most of my days volunteering at the kids' schools, and running them here and there. I was also very involved in our church, where Dan and I both worked with the youth group.

When Janet and Steve were both happily married to wonderful spouses, and David was in college I was 49 years old. At this point in my life things were looking good. Once we got David through college we would travel and enjoy life. I had a career that I enjoyed.

I was selling TV commercials. I had a wonderful husband. Life was hectic, but good. I enjoyed golfing, painting and crafts. I loved my job selling commercials for cable television. Unfortunately, it was at this time that I began to notice problems on my left side. It was subtle at first.

During my golf swing, my hand clamped shut. My left arm would not extend fully either. What's going on, I wondered? I went to an orthopedic doctor. The doctor gave me a needle in the hand and said, "Let's see if that helps." It did not.

Then I had a seemingly endless string of tests: MRI'S, CAT scans, blood work, x-rays etc. This went on for nine months. I went from one doctor to another. First, they theorized that I might have had a stroke. Then they thought it might be Multiple Sclerosis. Next they considered the possibility of a brain tumor.

It was hard going from test to test.

Finally, a definitive diagnosis came from a neurologist who specialized in Parkinson's research. When I asked how he could be so certain, the doctor admitted that there isn't any specific test for the diagnosis of Parkinson's. He said he was an expert in the field and he knew from an examination and my test results that I had Parkinson's.

I cried, and my husband Dan was devastated. But we pushed on. Initially, I must admit that I lived in a state of denial. I told myself that I'd be just fine.

Telling my children was very difficult. My son Steve and his wife Vicki were living close by with my beloved granddaughter, Monica. When I told them, I don't think they understood, at first, though Vicki is in the medical field and she was familiar with Parkinson's. They did their best to reassure me.

I decided to go to Florida, to see my youngest, who was in college, to give him the news. When I told him, though he was upset he was also full of hope. He even went out and bought me new shoes. He said I needed to change my shoe style and wear sneakers instead. David thought my walking problems would be helped with them. Well, I couldn't walk properly in sneakers. I needed a heel on my shoes. David insisted I try new shoes. He read up on everything he could, related to Parkinson's disease, and gave me advice. He did not understand, but he tried so hard. He loved me and was only trying to help.

I made the trip to see my daughter, who was living in another area of Florida, with my wonderful son-in law, Anthony, and my precious new granddaughter. They were surprised. They were saddened by the news. Nevertheless, they tried to remain calm and reassure me. They showed their love to me. They wanted to know what they could do to help. There was nothing they could do, except to love me. All my children had the same basic attitude. They said, "You're strong mom, you'll be fine." And they really believed it. After all I had never been sick. I had never had any significant health problems.

I started my Parkinson's drugs, I did yoga and I tried to take care of myself and life went on for the next few years as if nothing happened. I did walk with a slight limp and did have some problems with my hand.

Some of my fellow co-workers noticed my problem. They asked me if I had had a stroke. I started to question the Parkinson's diagnosis. I wondered whether or not I might actually have Lyme disease.

Then came a double whammy. As if Parkinson's was not enough to bear. I had another problem lurking in my body. We had sold our house and we were having a beautiful rancher built to move into. We were living in an apartment building while it was being built. It's funny, you wake up one day feeling fine—unaware that this was the day you could die.

It was a warm morning in May. It was the day after Mother's Day. I had just spent a wonderful Mother's Day with David and Janet's family. I was feeling good. I was walking my dog on that beautiful morning. I started to get out of breath as we walked up the hill. I began to feel nauseated. I went back into the apartment and called my friend Nancy. While I was talking to her, the sweats came, and then the classic pain in the arm, and I felt like a brick was on my chest. I said, "Nancy, I am having a heart attack and I have to go. I'm driving to the hospital."

"No, I'll call an ambulance," Nancy responded.

"No. I'm driving myself," I insisted and then hung up.

I then turned to my dog, Snickers and said goodbye. I loved her very much and felt that I would never see her again.

I got in my car and drove. It was only about a seven-minute drive. As I was driving I was praying. I recited the Twenty-Third Psalm:

The Lord is my Shepherd; I shall not want.
He maketh me to lie down in green pastures:
He leadeth me beside the still waters.
He restoreth my soul:
He leadeth me in the paths of righteousness for
His name' sake.

Yea, though I walk through the valley of the
shadow of death,
I will fear no evil: For thou art with me;
Thy rod and thy staff, they comfort me.
Thou preparest a table before me in the presence
of mine enemies;
Thou annointest my head with oil; My cup runneth
over.

Surely goodness and mercy shall follow me all the
days of my life,
and I will dwell in the House of the Lord forever.

I knew it was bad and the pain got worse, like a truck was on my chest. I thought I was going to die. I cried for my children's loss and Dan's and I wanted to hug them all one last time. I wanted to talk to them so bad, but the pain was crushing and I could not talk on the phone and drive. I pulled up in front of the emergency ward opened my car door cried out for assistance, "help me!" Then I passed out.

The next thing I remember is that I was in the emergency ward, my clothes being cut off of me. My dear husband was standing there. Nancy had called him at work. I felt myself drift. I saw a white light. I felt warmth like never before. I felt the Lord holding me and rocking me and I felt so good. I wanted to just stay there with the Lord—warm and cuddly. The doctors and nurses were all working franticly on me. The gift was about to expire.

Then I looked at Dan, and I said to the Lord, "If you want me to go with you I will, or if you want me to stay with Dan and the kids I would like that." There was some fear that cropped up inside of me when I imagined my family, until I heard His voice, comforting, "You're going back." I felt like I had been given a second gift of life.

At that moment I was not afraid to die. I wanted to go home to be with the Lord. There was not panic about my destination. I was going to heaven because as a young child I had made a commitment to the Lord. You should read John 3:16 in the Bible. What a peace I had. You will know what I mean. The verse says it all: "For God so loved the world he gave his only son. That whoever believes in him will not perish, but have everlasting life." What a peace I had.

But it was not God's plan for me to leave this world at that time. The doctors gave me a jugular injection at that point. This, they say, saved my life. It stabilized me so they said to Dan we have to MedEvac her to a hospital where they can work on her.

The Gift   Mary Hill

Then came the helicopter ride to Allentown Hospital. I must admit to feeling claustrophobic. The helicopter seemed small. They slid my bed under something and my legs were encased. I didn't like the feeling. And it made me susceptible to noticing other minor things that seemed big at the time.

For example, I noticed that the nurse and the pilot had helmets on. So I asked the nurse, "How come you and the pilot have helmets and I don't? Don't you care if we crash I don't have one?" I was just trying to make nervous conversation. He explained, "It's so the pilot and I can talk to each other. It gets very noisy." My response? "What if I want to talk?" He laughed and leaned toward me and said, "I will talk to you. Don't you worry." Then he held my hand, "You're doing great for someone who is having a heart attack. You're going to be just fine.

The helicopter *was* noisy. The ride was fast. We were there in about twelve minutes. We landed on the hospital roof. They whisked me away to the operating room. That's all I remember until I woke up.

After the angioplasty the doctor came in and announced that he had good news and bad news. "The good news is that your heart attack was on the side it was on. Otherwise, you would have died. One side was blocked 100% and the other 90%. We did triple stents in the side that was 100% blocked. On the other side, we will have to perform an open-heart bypass."

The surgeon went on to explain that when someone has coronary artery disease, the arteries that supply blood to the heart could get clogged. The option they used on one side is a minimally invasive treatment called angioplasty. During my procedure they inserted three stents into three

17

blocked arteries. These small metal tubes prop open the heart's blood vessels. On the other side, he explained, it was necessary to perform an open-heart bypass. That would include an eleven to twelve inch incision in the chest and splitting the breastbone. They then pull back the breastbone and ribs in order to gain access to the chest cavity. At that critical juncture, the functions of the heart are attached to a heart-lung machine. Then they will use the mammary artery in my chest and a vein from my leg and create a bypass around the blocked portion of the heart muscle." The doctor paused and then gave me the bottom line. "The bad news is that if you have a heart attack while waiting we will not be able to save you."

I had to rest and recover from the angioplasty, so in five days they could do the open-heart surgery.

Do you know how it feels to wait in your hospital room knowing if you could have a heart attack and that they couldn't save you if you did? It brings on a lot of soul searching.

The third day after the heart attack I woke up and looked at my stomach. It looked like I had a black bikini on. Of course, I knew this wasn't possible, so I called the nurse. She remarked that it looked like a hematoma. In fact, they called it a "bikini hematoma." The doctors felt it was from blood accumulating under the skin during my angioplasty. I didn't like it, but what could I do? Now I look back at my reaction and chide myself at how I was more concerned about the way it looked than anything. My reaction seems so vain in hindsight. But I think it is important to admit this kind of thinking, so that you, the reader, will know that it's not *that* unusual to have such thoughts. I'd prefer to forget my somewhat shallow reaction and remember the strength of the others that surrounded me at the time.

I will never forget how my husband, children and grandchildren all rallied around me during that time. My wonderful daughter took charge of scheduling people to see me. Scheduling was necessary because I had so much company at one time in my room and the nurses did not like that. My daughter came every day to see me, she had just had a baby and I kept telling her to go home to be with her newborn, but she insisted on staying with me. We grew a bond, this I will never forget.

My son David came every day on his way to work and his way home after work. We spent a lot of time bonding. These visits were important to me. My son Steve came several times and brought my grand children. My friends were wonderful. They surrounded me with love and caring. We shared in laughter and tears. I even had my realtor and good friend Linda bring me roof and color samples of siding to my room as the house was being built.

The next day things took a turn for the worse. I was feeling sick and the nurse said I had a fever. The doctors didn't know what was going on. They sent an infectious disease doctor to take a look at me.

I recall saying to him, "Do you think I got bad blood when they did the transfusions?" He assured me that if I had that I'd already be dead. "Comforting thought," I replied in tongue-in-cheek fashion.

To this day, this setback remains a mystery. They never found out what caused it. But two days later it was gone. It was a Friday and they said they would operate on Monday.

Not expecting an affirmative answer, I asked whether I could go home for the weekend, explaining that I couldn't really rest in the hospital.

They agreed and Dan took me home. Just driving in the car seemed so nice, the birds chirping and the fresh air. I was glad to be alive.

Then the next day my daughter Janet and son- in-law Anthony came to visit. David was there too. Of course my granddaughters came also. I was happy to see them. But as the day went by I was feeling sicker. I didn't tell anyone because I didn't want to go back to the hospital.

Despite my stubborn attitude, Janet noticed that I wasn't looking well. She put her hand on my head. "You're burning up!!"

Back to the hospital…

(So much for my relaxing weekend at home)

They still didn't know the cause, but in a few days it was gone and they scheduled the surgery. I told Dan and Janet and David that they had to be sure someone was with me all the time after my surgery. With a feeling of anxiety that was hard to put in words, I pled with them not to "let them keep the tubes down my throat too long." I hated that. I hated the thought and was afraid of gagging. I recalled the appendix operation when I was seventeen and shuttered at the thought of the stifling tubes down my throat.

Well the next thing I remember I was coming out of surgery, and in the recovery room. I had tubes down my throat, tubes draining my chest, tubes to breath and IV's all over.

Guess what my first thought was? I don't want everyone *seeing* me like this. Again, my vanity was in full flower.

No sooner had the thought entered my mind I saw Dan, Janet and David and I tried to give them signals by panicking and pointing to my throat. They *knew* what I wanted. David's response? "For the first time she can't yell at us." Then he said, "Mom, we can't do anything about it. The doctors say they *have* to stay in for a few days."

I was angry, but there was nothing I could do about it.

A few days later they took most the tubes out. Then I went into a coronary care unit room.

It was at this time that I remember a big German nurse came in my room. She proclaimed that I was going to get out of bed and walk that very day. In response, I told her in no uncertain terms that I was not about to get out of bed and walk. I knew that if I did that I would throw up. I explained to her that was feeling awful.

Nevertheless, she insisted and started to take my covers off. I leaned over the side of the bed and threw up all over her, including her shoes. She left the room and I never saw her again.

Let me tell you, it is horrific throwing up after your chest has been cut open. The pain was excruciating. The only word that I could seem to muster at the time to explain how I felt to others was the word "awful." I continued to vomit all day.

Dan still kids me about how I seemed to lock onto the word and use it over and over. Today he recalls that I would say it over and over while I was in the ICU.

I suppose it was the only word I could think of at the time. It was like I was so overwhelmed by the situation that my mind simply put up blinders to any other descriptions.

After a week I was finally allowed to go home.
Although going home was a relief, I was not able to eat or sleep in bed. I could not lay flat. I slept in a recliner.

Everything had a metallic taste. Dan tried to get me to eat. He tried everything, even my favorite chocolate candies tasted terrible. I could only drink instant breakfasts. That's all I lived on for a month. As you might imagine, I lost a lot of weight.

For me, one of the worst things was not being able to *taste*. I really missed the taste of food. I could smell coffee or cake cooking, but I could not taste it. Imagine the anticipation of good tasting food and then the disappointing drab reality. I feared that I would never get my ability to taste back. I did eventually. Thank God.

As if all this was not enough, my heart condition threw off my Parkinson's. To make a long story short, about three months later I wound up in a wheel chair. I could not walk. I was crawling from my bed to the bathroom, on hands and knees. I would take a few steps and then I would stop, frozen. The doctor explained that the heart attack affected my PD and caused havoc on my whole system.

Here we go again, I thought. What is going on? I talked to my general practitioner, Dr. Rodriguez. He was confident that he would get to the bottom of it and figure out the cause. He sent me to a specialist who said I had the freezing form of Parkinson's and need to be put on new meds. Gait freezing: "freezing" is a manifestation of akinesia (an inability to move). Gait freezing is characterized by an inability to move the feet which may worsen in tight, cluttered spaces or when attempting to initiate gait. At the time I was struggling with feelings of depression. I even considered suicide for the first time in my life. Prior to this time in my life I couldn't even imagine how someone could sink to that level. But I was so depressed I just wanted to end it.

Depression affects approximately fifty percent of Parkinson's disease patients. Its sidekick, anxiety, affects more than twenty-five percent of the PD population. Some patients who bouts with mild depression, others experience the extremes of long-term depression and profound anxiety.

Dr. Laura Marsh, a neuropsychiatrist at Johns Hopkins University, puts it this way: "There are many depressive sub-syndromes that affect Parkinson's disease patients' quality of life. However, depression and anxiety are treatable, and treatment reduces the burdens of [Parkinson's] disease." According to Dr. Marsh and other experts, other non-motor symptoms are often more troublesome than many of the hallmark symptoms of PD, such as tremors.

Depression also is found among many cancer victims. In fact, according to the American Cancer Society, the suicide rate among those suffering with cancer is ten times greater than the general population.

Multiple Sclerosis is no different. Fifty percent of those with MS experience depression according to a leading expert in the field, Dr. J. Lamar Freed of the American Psychological Association.

As you can see, depression is a side effect of many incurable illnesses, but we can deal with it as long as we recognize it is there. It can also be a side effect from your medicine.

I remember we went on vacation during that time to Branson, Missouri. We went with our good friends Judy and Walter. Judy was such a help to me, but I hated it. I hated how people looked at me. Many behaved as if I weren't even there. One instance of this sort of rude treatment stands out in my memory. We were in line to a show and an insensitive woman there told my husband that I needed a jacket. I informed her that, though I was wheelchair bound, I could still hear and talk. I was furious.

At the time some people told to me that they would have stayed home and not went. They thought I was brave to go. Yes, I suppose that I was. I like to travel and be with dear friends, so I tried to overcome. I wanted to live as normal a life as possible. However, the supposed solution to my problem often seemed more like another issue. One good thing came from all of this, we got the best seats in house being in a wheelchair.

Some Parkinson's meds can cause obsessive behavior problems. Some can cloud the mind. The medication I was on sure did. And I think it made me suicidal. I was really considering killing myself one time. My mind was a blur for an entire year. Thank God for my husband, because he recognized this and insisted that I get help. Again, we had to change meds.

I recommend that you go on the Internet and do a search using the phrase "Parkinson's and obsessive behavior." When you do, you will find article after article and blogs relating personal experiences. Since each case of Parkinson's is unique, you must pursue information that relates as specifically to your conditions as possible. The more educated you become on the subject the better at expressing your symptoms to your physician you will become. This is the key to finding the proper meds for you. This applies to any disease.

So now I'm doing better. Those who have not seen me in years say I look better than ever. Most of the time I feel good, but I get stressed every day at end of the day. My body cramps up and I have trouble moving. Sometimes my body is just so exhausted I can hardly move. I hate that feeling, but I just have to go to bed and sleep it off.

Going through rough times puts things into perspective.

I actually believe that my health issues, including Parkinson's, have been a blessing. It made me stop and think about the important things in life. I started to think about my time on earth. I was pushed into a painful corner where I was forced to consider whether I was making the best of my life.

I have always tried to help others. My battle with Parkinson's has given me a new understanding for people who are sick. As the old Cheyenne Indian saying goes, "Do not judge your neighbor until you walk two moons in his moccasins." If you've never had an incurable illness, it is hard to really relate to the debilitating experience.

Despite my condition, I have learned to thank God for my life, as it is. I think it's not the one I would have chosen. Don't misunderstand, I cried out to God. I screamed at him and told him on multiple occasions that I couldn't take it anymore. If it was up to me I would have chosen an easier life, health wise, and I would have missed out on all the blessings that came from the illness. This is my life and I would not trade it now. On the other hand I'm not trying to whitewash disease. Anyone who has suffered from it knows how terrible it can be. The cramping up is painful, along with many other issues. But we must concentrate on finding a cure and in the meantime relief from as many of the symptoms as possible, for this and other diseases that plaque us.

CHAPTER THREE

In today's busy times, we seem to seek simplicity. We want things to be easy to do. I thought about a simple plan that everyone would be able to follow to help them deal with Parkinson's—what I call, THE BIG FOUR.

I was telling my friend Linda about THE BIG FOUR one day, and she inquired, "Which of the steps are easy?"

Great question. *None*, of course, is the answer.

Although they may not easy to do, the steps are easy to follow.

MY FOUR TIPS FOR OVERCOMING AN INCURABLE DISEASE

1. Diagnoses and Doctor

2. Right Medicines

3. Exercise, Diet and Rest.

4. Attitude

Let's explore these four rules together.

1. Diagnoses and Doctor

The Doctor-Diagnoses Connection

You need to find a good doctor to be diagnosed properly.

I found a good general practitioner, Dr. Ulazawitz, seven years ago. When I went to him after the golfing incident when my hand cramped so severely that it would not open he vowed to find out what was wrong. He spent a lot of time with me, talking to me, asking about symptoms, and sending me from one specialist after another.

My advice to you is to find a good doctor who cares about you and spends time talking to you.

Today I have a great GP Dr. Rodriquez. He spends time with me, and I never feel rushed. If your doctor rushes you in and out and acts like he is too busy, you need to look elsewhere. He makes me feel like I'm important. He takes an interest in my life. He's good at figuring things out because he actually has taken the time to get to know me. Eventually, he could just look at me, ask questions and know what's wrong. "Dr. Rod," as I call him, always has the attitude that he can get to the bottom of whatever problem arises. His positive, problem-solving attitude has been a source of strength for me. Find a doctor who does not dwell on the negative.

I have a good neurologist, Dr. Barbour.

Interview your doctor ask him or her questions about your illness, find out how knowledgeable they are on the subject. This will help you to figure out how much time is he or she willing to take for you. A physician who is willing to go the extra mile is worth his weight in gold. Dr. Rod has gone the extra mile many times. He called my insurance company and stayed on the phone until he got me what I needed.

One time I went to a neurologist who was an expert in the field of Parkinson's, but he was into the research of the disease. He did not care for me. He did not spend the time with me I needed. Consequently, he missed some key factors in my health care. He did not inform me of the side effects of certain drugs.

Don't let that go on. Fire your doctor, if you have to. Your interest comes first. I think it's a good idea to find a doctor who specializes in your illness. Yes, you need to know some of the normal symptoms, but *you may not* experience *all* of them.

My doctor told me that the brain is the final frontier. There is still much research to be done on Parkinson's.

Take an active role in your treatment. Never totally trust their decisions. They might not know everything. In fact, in my experience the "know it alls" seldom do. Rather, the doctors that are a bit less cock-sure and more willing to explore other possibilities will serve you better. Parkinson's us too complex a disease and there is still so much that is not known, you should always be a bit wary of a doctor that seems to be a one-size fits all diagnosis type. You know your body best and if something is not right you *must* tell them. Ask questions. If it is a question of medicine, always be certain to inquire about the risks and side effects.

Just recently I found out I have carpal tunnel syndrome on my left hand. The test they give to determine involved needles in the hand and arm and electric shocks. Tests of this sort are never fun. The average test result is 45. Mine was 14.

I had a bad case because I let the hand pain and tingling go because I thought it was from the PD. I had the hand surgery done on my left hand and then on my right. They are much better already.

So once you have found the right doctor, then what?

2. Medicine

Finding the right medicine

Finding the right drugs can take a long time. Some drugs work better for some people and not on others.

It is trial and error for you and your doctor. You have to work with your doctor telling him or her all side effects you experience while taking the drug. Go on the Internet and look up the drug. There are a number of excellent sites where you can get all kinds of information, including feedback from other people that have been prescribed the same or alternative medications.

How a specific drug will affect an individual depends on that individual. While one drug causes very few side effects in a sufferer another drug may make life nearly unbearable.

Since Parkinson's is a motor-neural disease, many of the side effects associated with the various drugs involved in treating Parkinson's manifest in the brain and brain function.

Levadopa seems to be the most widely prescribed medication. It reduces tremors and helps with bradykinesia (Bradykinesia is slowness in the execution of movement). Levadopa works directly on the brain because it is converted to dopamine in the brain. Parkinson's sufferers often have very low levels of dopamine produced in the brain, so Levadopa can help.

Levadopa is regularly combined with a second drug called carbidopa, because Levadopa so often seems to provoke nausea.

Sadly, the major side effects experienced by so many people prescribed Levadopa are psychiatric. Levadopa can cause confusion and extreme emotional outbursts. It sure did have that affect on me. It can also cause one to have horribly vivid dreams and nightmares, visual and auditory hallucinations.

Also associated with the treatment of Parkinson's many report drowsiness, headaches, a decrease in saliva production, dizziness and even involuntary sleep attacks or sleep apnea. This is where an individual falls asleep without actually trying. Imagine being in the middle of a conversation when without any warning you simply drop off to sleep!

It's bad enough having Parkinson's. But Parkinson's compounded by negative side effects is really devastating. I experienced problems and side effects. I know about the horrible effects they can have, first-hand.

So be sure if you have any side effects to talk to your doctor about them. Reading the labels and information that often accompanies prescriptions is a must. If you go to the pharmacy to pick up medication and you discover that it is not accompanied by any literature, go out of your way to ask the pharmacist for literature. If your pharmacist doesn't have information, don't be afraid to pick his or her brain or ask where you could get literature.

Keeping a diary of your medication schedule is an excellent idea, particularly when starting a new drug or adjusting the dosing of your current medications. A diary can be a good way to help you and your doctor make medical decisions specific to your conditions. After all, with Parkinson's one size often does not fit all, as with most illnesses. I recommend that you keep a diary that includes the following:

- Take note of the times of day when you take your medications
- Record the times of day when you have good symptom control
- Write down which symptoms re-emerge during the day and when they come or go
- Every morning when you eat breakfast note what symptoms you experienced that night
- Be sure to take not of any complications you may experience, like dyskinesia, and their relation to when you take your medication or consume food and drink (it may be useful to note the timing of meals and snacks and whether this affects your symptom control)

Some people find it useful to create a numeric rating system to apply to their symptoms. Use a scale that is meaningful for you.

Some of the meds for heart are controversy.

I also recommend vitamins. Take a multi vitamin and cod liver oil pills for heart problems. You need to talk to your doctor, if your not eating right you might need more supplements.

Any medicine you take for any disease can have side effects. You need to be aware of them. Then you can determine if they are right for you.

I find I am a little hyper on my drugs but if I don't take them I get all stiff. I would rather be charged up than stiff. Maybe your doctor will ask if you will be involved in a study one of the drug companies is doing or some research is being done. I think it's a good thing to do, because you might be giving them some answers they need, to make a better drug.

3. Exercise, Diet and Rest

Maintaining mobility is one of the most important tasks for anyone fighting Parkinson's. You must be determined to continue regular daily activities. My doctors informed me that remaining mobile and active is especially critical during the early states of Parkinson's because it is important to establish the habit of physical activity early on. This is the same for most illnesses.

The Gift   Mary Hill

Despite my Parkinson's I am able to stand on one foot with my other foot extended to my thigh for minutes at a time. I can touch my toes.

I had a friend with Parkinson's who asked me to help her with yoga. At the time she could just about sit up. I gave her basic stretches to do starting by sitting on the floor wit her back up against the wall. She was able to do many more moves and to increase her limited flexibility.

Don't get me wrong. I can't put my legs over my head like a pretzel. I have no desire to do that. I can do "down dog" etc., and the "prayer position" as well as the deep breathing exercises though. These exercises help me to relax or deal with pain.

Yoga is wonderful exercise. It works both sides of the body equally. Yoga will help you maintain flexibility. That's important with all of us (over 40) and actually everyone needs to keep flexible. There are different types of yoga. There is meditation, low exertion, moderate exertion, and high exertion. I recommend moderate exertion. You might need to start with low exertion in the beginning. Get a CD or take a class. Start with it slow and easy. You don't have to be able to put your feet over your head, I can't. Start with basic stretching. Once you feel comfortable you will have a routine you can do in front of the TV etc. You only need to do it 3 times per week, 10-15 minutes to feel better. Walk, even if you can only take few steps at a time. I believe if you force yourself it *will* come. I was in a wheel chair a few years ago from my Parkinson's. Now I'm free of those shackles. I run circles around my family and friends, when I am up, meaning walking good and running like I am on high test.

Sure there are times I have trouble walking, but they are few because I force myself. I put one step in front of the other. One of the tricks my neurologist taught me is if you are walking and freeze up, try and step over lines on floor tiles etc. If there aren't any tiles or lines on the floor to concentrate on as miniature goals, just imagine them. THIS WORKS. You have to find what works best for you.

You absolutely need your sleep. Sleep is essential for anyone with an illness. Sometimes I like to stay up late till 2 a.m. on my computer or with my friends etc. I certainly don't recommend this to anyone else. I pay for it, and you will too. I can't usually do this without feeling stressed to the point of exhaustion, unless I take a rest time during day, I might not sleep but I lie down and relax.

So make sure you take a small snooze during the day if you're going to do that. Prior to the onset of Parkinson's, I never used to take some down time. Now I find the relaxation practically indispensable.

A year ago I was so hyper on my drugs I could not sleep and when I did sleep it really wasn't recuperative. You feel so much better when you can sleep well and your body heals more efficiently.

What you eat really is important. Take daily vitamins. Eat fruit. Eat fiber to keep you regular. Drink green tea, or white tea. Both are high in antioxidants. Yes caffeine is not bad. Caffeine stimulates the brain to produce dopa in your brain. But depending on your illness it might not be best for you. So check with your doctor.

I would recommend eating a lot of small meals during day instead of three big ones. You should eat a lot of roughage and fruit, unless your illness requires that you don't. Constipation can result from Parkinson's, or from drugs used to treat the illness. It can also be the result of a lack of activity and movement. For this reason you should cultivate high-fiber diet. Dietary supplements such as psyllium or stool softeners can help regulate bowel movements as well. Related to constipation issues, although not restricted to being of value in solving problems with constipation is the need to increase daily fluid intake, especially in hot climates. Your goal should be to consume at least six cups of liquid should be drunk daily.

Constipation can be caused by the slowing down of the muscle action in the digestive tract, something that can be a natural consequence of Parkinson's disease. Peristalsis, the unhealthy slowing of the movement of food through the gut, is often a result of a combination of the disease itself and the medications used to treat it. This problem can be found in a lot of illnesses.

You don't want to be overweight. It's not healthy. I try to eat healthy. I always have. I keep my weight down, and in the last few years, I've become the slimiest I've ever been. I feel so much better with a slimmer physique.

On the other hand, some who suffer from Parkinson's can experience the opposite tendency. Often people loose the desire to eat and many loose too much weight. Loosing muscle weight can be a real problem. Why this occurs has something to do with the way Parkinson's sufferers' bodies digest food. People with Parkinson's can experience problems absorbing nutrients. If you experience any problems with weight loss, it is important to notify your doctor right away. You may actually need to put on weight.

You may even be loosing too much weight in an unintentional manner, due to a combination of factors, such as a loss of taste, sense of smell and/or appetite, feelings of nausea, difficulty swallowing etc.

The best remedy to this situation is to become directly involved in your daily consumption habits. Make it a point to know everything that goes into your system. Taking an active roll in the preparation of food is a big help. If you haven't taken control of the preparation of your food it is less likely that you will develop control over your consumption of food.

I enjoy cooking and especially love soup. Soup, whole wheat bread and *green* salads are an ideal combination for me. Some people say to me, "I can't make soup." *Yes* you *can*. It's easy. Here are a few simple examples for you to try. Enjoy.

Vegetable Rice Soup

2 lbs. of beef cubes, browned in skillet
Place in large pot on stove
Add 3 cups water and 1 finely chopped up onion (use a food chopper)
1 large can of crushed tomatoes
A pinch of salt & pepper
Cook until meat is tender
Add 1 bag of frozen vegetable (for soup)
Add ½ cup brown rice
Let simmer for 1 hour

Chicken Noodle Soup

The Gift   Mary Hill

2 lbs. of chicken legs and thighs
3 carrots, pealed and sliced
1 onion finely chopped
2 stalks of celery chopped
1 tbs. dried or fresh parsley
2 chicken bullion cubes
Salt & pepper to taste
1 bag of thin noodles or 1 lb. box of Ditalini noodles

Put chicken in large stockpot fill 2/3 with water. Add all
ingredients except noodles
Boil until done.
Take chicken out and de-bone the meat.
Place the meat back in pot
Add the noodles and boil for 5 minutes
Serve soon after

Mary's Chili

2 lbs. of ground turkey
1 tbs. EVOO (Extra Virgin Olive Oil)
1 onion
2 cloves garlic
2 tbs. chili powder
2 tbs. cumin
1 tbs. crushed red peppers
1 tsp. salt & pepper
1/2 tsp. sugar
4 large cans of crushed tomatoes
3 15 ½ oz. cans of red kidney beans

Brown the turkey in a large pot with next 8 ingredients.
When it is cooked add the cans of tomatoes
Simmer for 1/2 hour
Add beans cook 15 more minutes
(the ground turkey is healthy substitute for red meat)

Healthy Turkey Tacos

1 lb. ground turkey (lean)
1 tsp. cumin
2 tsp. chili powder
1 tsp. dried hot peppers
¼-cup water

1 package of 12 fresh tortillas
1 tomato, finely chopped
1 onion, finely chopped
Lettuce, sprinkled with Italian dressing
1 lb. of sharp cheese shredded
Taco sauce

In large skillet brown 1lb of ground turkey in 1 tsp oil
Add next 3 ingredients. Add water, cover simmer

In small skillet pour oil until covers bottom of pan.
Set on high heat, when hot drop tortillas in oil fold in half.
Quickly turn on each side in hot oil.
Drain on paper towels.

Serve with the next ingredients. Make your own tacos
Delicious!!!!!!!!!

Mary's Spaghetti Sauce

1 tbs. olive oil
2 clove garlic
1 lb. ground beef (lean)
2 lg. cans crushed tomatoes
1 lg. can of tomato sauce
2 tsp. crushed hot peppers
2 tsp. basil
2 tsp. oregano
A pinch of salt & pepper

Brown the meat and garlic in oil in large stockpot
When brown, add the cans of tomatoes and next ingredients
Simmer 1/2 hour

In addition to soup, here are a few more miscellaneous recipes for you to try:

Apple Salad

Cut 1 apple up into small pieces
Add ¼ cup walnuts
1 tbs. raisins
A spoon full of chopped dates

I love this and it is good for you. You can add 1 tbs. whipped cream or miracle whip.

Apple Crisp

Spray Pam on a small square pan
Slice 4 good-sized apples
Lay them in pan
In a bowl add the following:
Soften a ½ stick of butter
½ cup oats or one serving size of instant oatmeal
A dash of cinnamon
½ cup flour
Mix together, sprinkle over apples
Bake at 375 degrees for 15-20 minutes

Note: Eat when hot and add a dip of low fat ice cream to
make it extra yummy.

4. Attitude

Be positive

I saved the best and most important for last.

What does the word *fulfilled* mean? The meaning is "to bring into actuality, to carry out, to complete." These are the meanings in the dictionary. Why can't you bring into actuality your goals in life and carry them out? Just because you have an illness doesn't mean you should shrivel up and die. Believe me, sometimes I feel like that, but I know it will do me no good. Instead, I make goals and try and achieve them. If they are daily goals or yearly goals it's the same thing. You should start out with daily goals. Maybe you want to learn something new, like how to play Texas hold'em—something I got interested in last year. Maybe you want to just get out of bed and go for a walk. My husband and I try to take a walk with our dog Snicks. Snickers and Dan sometimes can walk further than me, but I can walk faster once I get into gear. I just can't stop once I get going.

Set your mind to accomplish what you need to do. Your brain is powerful. You can control it. When I went to see one doctor, when I couldn't walk, she took sticks and laid them on the ground and asked me to walk over them. At the time I was in a wheel chair and could hardly take a step. I walked right over those sticks. She said to think of sticks on the ground if I can't walk. It has helped me many times to do that. Don't get me wrong. There are days I just want to have a pity party. I don't walk around smiling all the time. I like to paint sometimes and when I do I feel good. I will do an acrylic painting in one or two days. I have a lot of energy and I am on a high from my prescription drugs. When I get that dopamine, watch out! I find it hard to sit still sometimes. But I force myself to.

My friends and family, they are an important part of living a good life. I have been blessed with great friends like my dear friend Judy. We have been through much together in the last twenty years or so. I have a good friend Joanne who is going through a hard time now in her life with cancer. I try to help her as much as possible. We have been friends for 20 years or so also. We try to encourage each other. We understand because we both are going through rough times. My friend Kathy is in the same situation, we have been friends over 20 years. My family is great. My husband is there for me and helps me whenever I need him. He recently retired early so he could be there for me. My kids are constantly there for me and are a real encouragement to me.

If you keep a good attitude it will help you thru the rough times. It's hard for me. Every morning I wake up feeling nauseated. I don't want to eat. I have problems walking, getting one step in front of the other. I push myself.

I am a Christian with very strong beliefs. Divine Providence is with me every day. I count on my faith to keep me true. God has never failed me yet, and I know He never will.

I have a good support group, my family and friends. I am fortunate in this respect. If you don't have friends, make it a practice to gather them like beautiful, fragrant flowers.

Remember, to have friends you have to be a friend. Be a friend to someone else. Help them with *their* problems. You will get more joy from helping others. Avoiding being so self-absorbed will go a long way in actually helping you feel better.

Have Faith

Have faith too. Find the friend who is always present. Experience faith in God. Go to church. Read your Bible. You will feel much better. Friends and pleasant distractions and service to others can be readily found in doing so.

I found Romans 8:28 and 29 to be a help to me.

> *"And we know that **all things work together for good to those who love God, to those who are the called according to His purpose**. For whom He foreknew, He also predestined to be conformed to the image of His Son."*

I also poured over the book of Job in the Bible. When Job questioned God about his plight God answered something like this: "How can you ask me why? Where were you when I put the stars in place? Where were you when I created the earth? Where were you when I put you in your mother's womb? I have a plan for your life that is beyond your limited, finite capacity to understand.

I can't do a better job than God. That's when I gave it all to him. I put it all in his hands, and decided to not worry so much about my life. I decided to let GOD. This has changed my life so much. It gives me a peace in times of anxiety. When you find faith you will have peace.

This has helped me realize that God has a plan and purpose for *my* life. His plan is better than any plan I could have. I try not to question Him any more. In the beginning of my tribulations I certainly did question Him. I remember screaming at the top of my lungs, "GOD why are you doing this to me? You must have me mixed up with another Mary Hill. Remember me? I'm the Mary Jane Hill, born April 1951. You say you won't give us more than we can bear. This is more than I can bear!"

God answered my cry, assuring me that He knew my physical, mental and spiritual fabric. He let me know that He knew what was best for me and I began to understand that my condition could very well possibly be the best possible situation considering how bad things could be. He also filled me with the warmth of His love. I knew that Jesus understood every aspect of the human condition, having had the sins of the world piled on Him, yet He was triumphant.

Faith is defined as "a belief that does not rest on logical truth or evidence." During my times of illness I have relied on my faith in the Lord. I read the book of Job. The whole book was an inspiration, but what hit me was when Job questioned God on why this was happening to him. God answered something like this: "Where were you when I put you in your mothers womb? Where were you when I made the heaven and the earth? Where were you when I put the stars in place? Why question me?"

The book of Job helped me to gain much needed perspective. I knew then that God had a purpose and a plan for my life. He was in charge. Who am I to question Gods plan? I can't do a better job than God. That's when I gave it all to him. I put it all in His hands, and decided to not worry so much about my life. I decided to "let go and let GOD." You see, I had made a very important commitment to the Lord at age seven. I gave him my life. I told him I believed he was God's son and died on the cross for my sins. I became one of His.

This attitude of faith has changed my life so much. It gives me a peace in times of anxiety. When you find faith you will have peace.

Here are some valuable scriptures related to attitude's relationship to faith that have helped me:

"And we know that all things work together for good to them that love God and are called according to his purpose."
Romans 8:28

"Above all else, guard your heart, for it is the wellspring of life."
Proverbs 4:23

"When a man is gloomy, everything seems to go wrong; when he is cheerful (and full of hope), everything seems right."
Proverbs 15:15

"A cheerful heart is good medicine."
Proverbs 17:22

"A man's spirit can sustain his broken body, but when spirit dies, what hope is left?"
Proverbs 18:14

"You, Lord, give perfect peace even in turmoil to those who keep their purpose firm and put their trust in you."
Isaiah 26:3

The Gift   Mary Hill

*"So take a new grip with your tired hands, stand firm on
your shaky legs, and mark out a straight, smooth path for
your feet so that those that follow you, though weak and
lame, will not fall and hurt themselves, but become
strong."*
Hebrews 12:12

*Humble yourselves, therefore, under God's mighty hand,
that he may lift you up in due time. Cast all your anxiety
on him because he cares for you.*
I Peter 5: 6-7

The Gift   Mary Hill

Smile

Practice at smiling in order to feel better. A friend, Michele said to me, "Mary, you don't smile much." From that day on I decided to try and smile more. I decided to make it a habit. Give it a shot. It works.

Is the glass half empty or half full? Perspective determines how we feel about the world around us.

Remaining positive, particularly when negative experiences beset us always makes life easier to manage. Each moment we exude positivism is a small triumph that we can take pride in.

Smiling when we feel like frowning, laughing when we feel like crying, and participating when we'd rather be alone, brooding and feeling sorry for ourselves buoys the spirits.

You should also consider how we mirror the attitudes of others. Surround yourself with people that are realistically positive. I'm not talking about "pie in the sky" folks that are so "out there" that they are no practical good, rather, those whose attitude is infectious and who more often opt for solutions over disabling emotions. We're disabled enough as it is with Parkinson's and other illnesses. Let's not compound our problem by "woe is me" negativity.

I assure you that it will be easier to feel better about your situation when you can feed off of the nutrients of positive folk, pro-active activity, engagement and faith.

Choose the happier thought

When you're faced with a bad feeling or negative thought, find an equally true thought about the situation that makes you feel better. I don't mean you should deny the negative—just pay more attention to the positive part of the truth. Example: sometimes when I having a dinner party I think, "I can never get this dinner party done in time." And I start to panic. Then I take a deep breath and say to myself. Yes I can because I have done it before and I can do it again. The more I relax and do this the more ideas flow, and I feel better. You will also, if you do this.

The Gift   Mary Hill

Train your brain

Our habits do affect our happiness, and neuroscientists have recently found out why. Habitual thoughts and behavior create specific neural pathways in the wiring of our brains. The process can be compared to the way water flows downhill and creates a groove in the earth.

When we think in a certain way over and over, the neural pathway becomes stronger as the groove gets deeper. Scientists used to think these neural pathways were set in stone. But now research shows that when you repeatedly think, feel and act in a different way the brain is able to rewrite itself. Scientists call this phenomenon "brain plasticity."

So you can actually change your level of happiness. How can this help us who have incurable diseases? Think positive. Think you *can overcome* and maybe you will. Think happiness and you just might be able to train your brain to start to feel happy again.

Let me tell you a story I once heard. I am a small part American Indian, Delaware. So this story really sums it up.

One day an old Cherokee elder told his grandson about the battle that goes on inside people's heads. "My son," the elder explained, "there are two wolves that live inside all of us. One is unhappiness, fear, worry, jealousy, and self-pity. The other is happiness, joy, love hope, truth and compassion."

The little boy thought for a few minutes. Then he asked, "Which wolf will win?"

The old Cherokee simply responded, "The one you feed."

I love this analogy. Make sure you fed the right one.

Have friends

A UCLA study showed that men and women release adrenaline and cortisol when under stress. A woman's brain also releases oxytocin, the bonding hormone. That's why women who are going through a rough time want to have long "talk fests" with a girlfriend. The more they engage in bonding activities, the more oxytocin they release, which produces a calming effect. So when your upset or stressed and you don't have time for family and friends, think again, this is when you need them. Interesting is a recent Gallup management Journal article. When you acknowledge those around you -dopamine is released-a neurochemical that's directly linked to being happy. It is also the neurochemical that is directly linked to Parkinson's, a lack of. This is an interesting concept I intend to read up on. So friends and loved ones so important in our lives. Having good social relationships is a strong reason for happiness.

The Gift   Mary Hill

Find Passion & Purpose

I am passionate in everything I do. I try to have a sense of passion about my mundane activities. Doing so boosts my happiness. Every job I had I tried to think of as an adventure.

An example of getting passionate about mundane activities is a story I'll share with you. Years ago when we were having a house built and we had 3 kids. We had to all live in a Holiday Inn for a week. I had all three children in different schools, High school, Middle school and kindergarten. I had to drive them all to there schools and then pick them up after. I said to them this is an adventure. My husband went to work all day. My work seemed to be chauffeuring kids all day. I made a big deal out of eating cereal in the morning out of those little boxes you cut open and pour the milk in and eat right out of the box. My two boys thought it was cool, but my daughter was in high school and this was not cool, including all sharing a bathroom. But telling the kids this is a great adventure, even when we were kicked out of Holiday Inn and had to find another hotel, due to a conference they had that week. Let me also share a story I read once. This is another example of what I mean. One day an old lady walked to a building site where three men were laying bricks. She asked the first man what are you doing? He said Lady I'm laying bricks can't you see? That's what I do, lay bricks. She walked to the second man and asked the same question. I'm a bricklayer and I take pride in my work, and it feds my family. Then she asked the same question to the third man. I am building the most beautiful church you have ever seen. So I suggest you think about what activities most absorb you and analyze what it is about them that makes you happy.

CHAPTER FOUR

INTERVIEWS

I had the privilege of interviewing some wonderful people who face life everyday with incurable illnesses. What I learned might be a help to you. Each of these people all have uplifting spirits—people who handle their illness in a positive way. Maybe we can learn from them.

Pat Maslovch

When Pat enters a room she has an air of confidence about her, that all is well.

Mary: What illness do you have?
Pat: MS
Mary: Are you on a special diet?
Pat: Low fat and cut out gluten (all white bread and pasta) I am not real strict though
Mary: When were you diagnosed?
Pat: In 1970
Mary: How did you find out?
Pat: I had a spinal tap. If they see 3 lesions on the spine they consider it MS.
Mary: How did it affect you?

Pat: I had to stop working and went on disability. I still did some work at home for a short time, though I would get fatigued and tired so I had to quit.

I was diagnosed in 1975 and went into remission for a brief time in 1993. I worked for a large chemical company. Many friends were losing their jobs. I was upset. They say one of the causes is stress. I think that had something to do with it.

I had a relapse in 1993.

Mary: Do they know the cause of MS?

Pat: The lesions look like little lights in the receptors of the brain. I call them "Pac men." When I am having problems I say the "Pac men" are busy.

Mary: What helps you do so well?

Pat: I am doing better after going on a Beta serum injection, every other day. Some people do not do well on this. I am doing well on it.

It has helped me tremendously.

Mary: What obstacles have you had to overcome?

Pat: Many. Dealing with vanity, for instance. I gained weight when I was on a steroid. I have since lost it.

Mary: Do you suffer from depression?

Pat: Yes, in the beginning I was having pity parties all the time. I was always talking about MS. One day my husband said to me, "You're letting the disease control you instead of you control the disease." So I decided to fight.

One day I was looking at a prayer plant, they open up beautifully on little support. I decided then and there that if they could do it so could I. It was a turning point. I was told to go to a support group. I visited people with MS that were in bad shape, some died. This made me more depressed. Some times the support groups were so negative they made me depressed.

I decided to start my own support group. The MS foundation trained me. I try to keep the meetings positive. In my meetings I allow 1/2 hour to talk about *positive* information.

One time, at a meeting, I had people from the MS society in Germany discuss how chronic diseases were treated there. We found out that in Germany at age 50 a person with MS has their prescriptions cut off by the government (socialized medicine).

Mary: What activities do you do?

Pat: I golf. I have a red flag on my golf cart that allows me to get closer to the greens. I walk.

Mary: How do you deal with others that have the same disease—those with more advanced stages of MS?

Pat: I visited a friend who has MS and she was at death's door. It was so hard for me to see because I was told you don't die from MS.

My friend can't walk. She is strong-willed so she got a service dog. The dog has been a great help to her. She now gets around a little. Some people will be worse than you, whatever your illness. You have to overlook that. We are all different & unique.

All is not perfect. I struggle every day.

Mary Ann Bedard

When Mary Ann enters a room she looks so healthy. She has a kind spirit about her. On the day we met and I interviewed her she had just come from chemo. She let me know that things may have been different if the interview had been one day later. She usually gets sick the day after treatment. They were trying a new chemo today.

Mary: When were you diagnosed?
Mary Ann: December 2001. Breast cancer.
Mary: How old were you?
Mary Ann: I was 61 and healthy, up to that point.
Mary: Did you have surgery?
Mary Ann: Yes, I had a mastectomy in December. Then in January they found a spot on my lung. In February I had the upper lobe in my right lung removed. They said I had two separate cancers. I never took it real serious. I always thought I would be fine. And I did well.
Mary: How was your attitude?
Mary Ann: Life is a gift and I live every day to the fullest.
Mary: How do you handle depression?
Mary Ann: I have a sleep mechanism in me; I go to sleep until I feel better. I do not take medicine for depression.
Mary: Something happened in August 2006?
Mary Ann: Yes, in August of 2006 they found a spot on my left lung and back. The doctors said they were too small to be dangerous.

Then they did lung surgery and found out it was stage four breast cancer in my lungs and I have bone cancer lesions all over.

Mary: What treatment are you receiving?
Mary Ann: I am on hormone shots and bone enhancer into the liver. This is a new treatment I hope it does well for me.
Mary: How are you handling this?
Mary Ann: I take my condition more serious now. It's overwhelming. I never thought of dying before.
I now realize what I have and appreciate each day.

Peter W. Houck

Mary: What illness do you have?
Peter: Rheumatoid arthritis, Fascitis Myalgia syndrome.
Mary: When were you diagnosed?
Peter: In 1989.
Mary: What are your symptoms?
Peter: I have a hard time getting up. Walking is painful. Just getting out of bed is painful.
Mary: What meds do you take?
Peter: I take 13 meds and 12 vitamin and minerals. The meds include Prednisone, which is a steroid. I have been on that for since 1989.
Mary: Do you ever get depressed?
Peter: Yes. The biggest thing is you can't do the things you used to be able to do. Like just getting up can be a major problem. Putting your shoes on can be a project.
Mary: How do you handle that?
Peter: You *have* to exercise and keep moving. When I get sick and have a bad day I have to take several days after that to rest. You get used to living with the pain and try to block it out of your mind.
Mary: What obstacles have you had to overcome recently?
Peter: Recently, I had the shingles in my upper right eye area. I lost some sight in my eye. I was in the hospital for a week. While I was there they gave me the wrong medicine. I was so sick, I went from 185 to 160 pounds in a day. I even lost the fat in my feet, so my bones are more exposed, and every step I take hurts. You just block it out and keep going. You try to train your brain, as you say in your book, Mary.

Mary: How is your life different now?
Peter: With my disease my resistance is low and I have
to be careful not to get sick. Now that I am not working it
is easier. When I worked some days I would cramp up so
badly that I could hardly make it home. Now when I get off
schedule or forget my pills I cramp up. Then I have to wait
for my meds to kick in.
Mary: You have a great attitude. What do you attribute it
to?
Peter: I was always a fighter. Now that I'm retired I
enjoy life more and appreciate it so much more. You
realize nothing material really maters. I'm just happy to be
alive. When I see others who are worse off than I, I feel
lucky. I enjoy life, despite my troubles. I'm active. I go to
church. I volunteer at the church. I do renovations on my
home. I have a new toy—a tractor front-end loader. I love
'playing' on it. I like to help others and make them happy. I
have a wonderful wife who is so supportive. Life is worth
living, but I'm not afraid to die when the time comes. I
hope I go fast.

Kathie

Kathie is a long-time friend of mine.
She is a woman of strong faith.

Mary: What were you diagnosed with?
Kathie: Severe Asthma. My asthma is bad enough to be considered one of the top twelve worst by my doctor.
Mary: When?
Kathie: September 2000. I had asthma before that time, but on mild level.
Mary: What happened to change it?
Kathie: Chronic exposure to perfume in my job caused acute reactions.
Mary: What were the acute reactions?
Kathie: Coughing, shortness of breath and dizziness. Then other triggers started from industrial fumes.
Mary: How has this affected your life?
Kathie: Socially, I have had to abstain from all social functions, including church. I now "do church" on the web. This makes my life difficult for friendships, work etc. People don't understand the severity of my illness. When they use fragrance I can't be around them. This includes medical care. Medical professionals wear fragrances too sometimes. If I'm going to hospital for treatment they have to know to be perfume free.
I used to take my freedom of everyday activities for granted.
Mary: How do you deal with this?
Kathie: Through trial and error I find places I can go. I focus on what I *can* do. I also use a mask, and I carry a

breathing machine wherever I go. I try not to go places alone, in case I have a breathing problem.

Mary: How do you deal with depression?

Kathie: I work out regularly. When I get depressed I have a short pity party, then get over it. Having a positive attitude makes all the difference.

Mary: What have you learned from this experience?

Kathie: God has assured me that He will be with me through any attacks and never leave me. And I have angels around me. They might be a real person or spiritual being.

Mary: Has this strengthened your faith?

Kathie: Yes it has. It has increased my prayer life. I spend more time praying. God numbers my days, and I am on this earth for a reason—like you, Mary. Who am I to question God? I take life one breath at a time.

Joanne:

Mary: What disease do you have?
Joanne: Breast cancer.
Mary: When were you diagnosed?
Joanne: July 7, 1995.
Mary: What treatment did you receive?
Joanne: Lumpectomy and radiation. I've been on Tamoxifen for five years.
Mary: How were you doing until recent times?
Joanne: I did fine until July 2007.
Mary: What happened?
Joanne: They found a lump and I was diagnosed with recurrent breast cancer. It spread to my bones.
Mary: What is your treatment for that?
Joanne: Chemo, once per week.
Mary: How do you deal with depression?
Joanne: I take one day at a time. My faith in God gets me through. Jeremiah 29:11 says it all: "For I know the plans I have for you plans to prosper you and not to harm you, plans to give you a hope and a future."
Mary: What makes you feel better and able to deal with this?
Joanne: I have so many friends and family members that support me. I like getting cards and phone calls.

I have been able to help others with cancer. I am a breast cancer volunteer. I deliver pillows to breast cancer patients for them to put under there arms after surgery.
Mary: How are you doing now?
Joanne: Recent scans show no progression of cancer. The Lord is good.

REVIEW

- *Surround yourself with those you love.*

- *Keep close to people who have a positive attitude.*

- *Keep focused on taking care of yourself.*

- *Count your blessings each day.*

- *Trust in God to be your rock.*

- *Take advantage of support groups.*

- *Read everything you can on your health issue*

The Gift   Mary Hill

Notes:

Notes:

Notes:

The Gift   Mary Hill

FIRST ORR BOOKS EDITION, 2008

Printed in the United States
203124BV00001B/31-240/P

9 780980 061178